GINN Spelling

Stage C

Book 1

GINN

Meet Inspector Spellwell

Look   Say   Cover   Write   Check

"Hello. I'm Inspector Spellwell. This is my team. We are looking for letter patterns."

We must look at the letter patterns in words to help us spell well.

"I can see the same letter pattern in the words 'spell' and 'well'."

What is the letter pattern?

Look again at these two words.

spell	well
sp/ell	w/ell

2

Add these single letters to the 'ell' letter pattern and write the words.

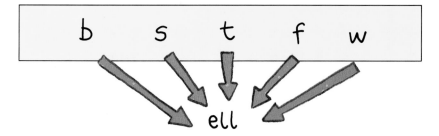

Here are some double letters to add to the 'ell' letter pattern. Write the words.

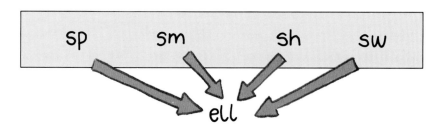

Write these words.

yellow   hello   jelly   cellar

satellite   dwelling   wellingtons   spelling

Find and circle the 'ell' letter pattern in each word.

Case closed

Look for letter patterns in words.

3

Vowels and consonants

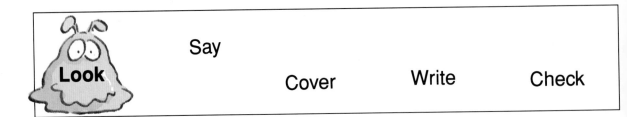

Look   Say   Cover   Write   Check

Five letters in the alphabet are very special.
They are called **vowels.**
All the other letters are called **consonants.**

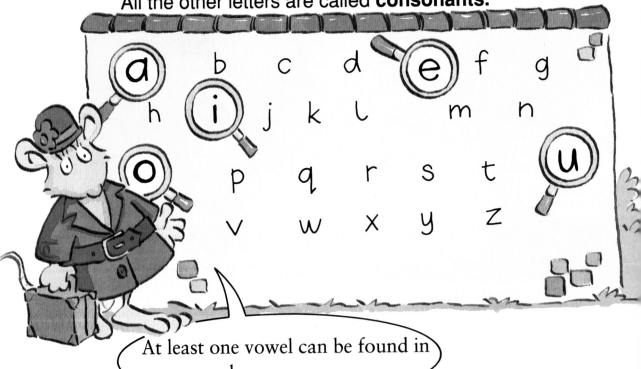

At least one vowel can be found in every word.

Write out this message and circle all the vowels.

Pick a bit of litter up.

Put it in a litter bin.

4

Now write this secret message and fill in the missing vowels.
The message will help you with spelling.

L _ _ k,   s _ y,

c _ v _ r,   wr _ t _,

ch _ ck.

Challenge

Make up a message for your partner.
Colour over all the vowels so they are hidden.
Challenge your partner to write out the secret message correctly!

Case closed

Look carefully at words.

All words are made up of vowels and consonants.

Each word must have at least one vowel in it.

Short and long vowels

What a difference an 'e' makes!

We don't always say the 'e' at the end of words.
But the 'e' can make a big difference to a word.
Say these words and see.

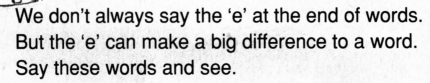

mad → mad e))

fin → fin e))...

not → not e))..

cut → cut e))....

When you add an 'e' to these words the vowel sound
changes so that the letter says its name.
It changes from a short to a long vowel sound.

Copy this table and finish it.

First word	Add an 'e'
win	wine
pin	
din	
shin	
spin	

Say the words and see what a difference
an 'e' makes!

Watch out!
The Letter Snatcher's about!
He loves stealing 'e's from the end of words.

Look at the words in the boxes below.

Say them aloud.

Cover them.

Write them without copying.

Check them afterwards.

hide	mane	mope	hate
ride	cane	hope	mate
slide	pane	slope	fate

Now write the words again with the 'e's missing.
Write a Handy Hint to explain what you discover.

Handy Hint

But not every word acts like this.

Look

| imagine | come | give | done |

'Y' as vowel and consonant

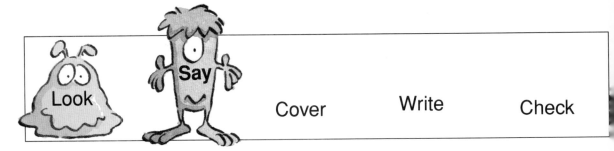

Look Say Cover Write Check

Don't be caught out by the letter 'y'.

In some words 'y' is a consonant.
In other words it can act as a vowel.

Remember: all words must have at least one vowel.

Look at these words.

try	you	yellow
my	why	yacht

Copy this table and put in the words above.

Words with vowels	Words where you can't see a vowel
you	my

Say the words in the table.
What sound does the letter 'y' make?
How does it change?

8

When 'y' sounds like 'eye'
it is pretending to be an 'i'.

It is disguised as a vowel.

Say the words on the wanted poster.

Reward

Wanted !

Find the words which use
a 'y' disguised as an 'i'.

cry	yes	sty
your	dry	yogurt
by	year	shy
fly	sky	yesterday

Without copying, write the words where
'y' is in disguise as an 'i'.

Case closed

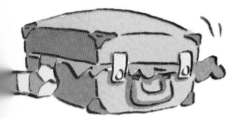

Sometimes 'y' can be a vowel.
Sometimes 'y' can be a consonant.

Saying the word can help you decide.

Monster words

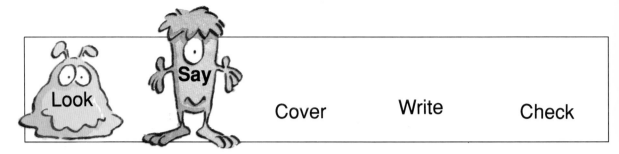

Look   Say   Cover   Write   Check

Look at the words the monsters are saying.
Each one is made up of letter patterns.

Say the words in a monster voice.

grup   grag   grup   glot   glot   grag

Make up some more monster words.
Take a letter pattern from the red box and
add it to one in the yellow box.
See how many monster words you can make.

pr	cl
	sh
sm	gl
st	

imp	ug
	ush
um	
ag	osh

Make a list of your five favourite monster words
from the words you made up.

Here are some real words.
Say each word slowly.

stand   black   spell   trip   grow

clock   print   drink   snap

Listen carefully to how you say the words.

Break each word into two letter patterns
and say it again.

Now write the words in their two letter patterns,
like this.

$$sp + ell = spell$$

Case closed

**Sometimes saying a word
slowly and clearly can
help you spell it.**

Tricky words: some, any, every

Pick out the word from each jar.

Some   any   every

Say each word.

Cover each word.

Write each word without copying.

Check your spellings against the words in the jars.

Which words are not spelt as they sound?

Sometimes the sound of a word can be misleading.

Make as many new words as you can by joining
'some' and 'any' to different words in the bags.

Write the new words you have made in a
chart, like this.

Some	Someone
any	anyone

Challenge How many new words can you make that
start with 'every'?

Letter patterns with 'ee' and 'oo'

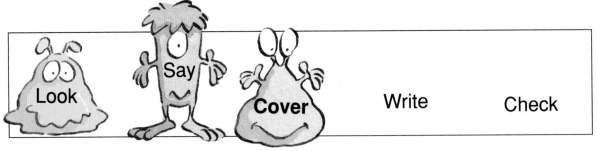

Look Say **Cover** Write Check

asleep crook peep creep look

book

sweep

Discover the words my undercover agent has left in the park.

Write the words in your book.

Challenge

Look carefully at the words

Try to sort them into 'eep' words and 'ook' words

Cover them with your hand.

Write the words in the two groups without looking back at them.

Check your words against the right spellings.

Hands off!

The letter patterns 'eep' and 'ook' have been covered up here.

Uncover the words by writing them out in full.

ed   k   st   j

wing   stle   sh   mist

Look carefully at these words.

mood	moody	good	goodness	wood
wooden	feed	feeding	greed	greedy
	need	needle		

Say all the words.
Cover the words with your hand.
Write them.
Ask a friend to check your spelling.

Case closed

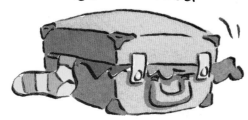

Try not to copy words.

Cover them and try to write them from memory.

15

Verb endings 'ing' and 'ed'

Watch out!
The Letter Snatcher's about!

We can change verbs by adding
different endings to them.

Root verb	Ending	New word
play	+ ing	= playing
play	+ ed	= played

But be careful with verbs that end
with the letter 'e'.

I often snatch the 'e' before
you can add 'ing' or 'ed'!

live + ing	= living
live + ed	= lived

Now try these.
The first one has been done for you.

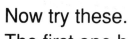

Root verb	+ ing	+ ed
like love save chase wipe scare	liking	liked

Challenge   Look at these words.

In some the root verb ends in an 'e'.
In others it doesn't.

Write the root verb for each.

Compound words

Sometimes you can make a new word by putting two small words together.

in side → inside

my self → myself

Each magnet will attract a word to make a bigger word.

Without copying, write the new words you can make.

foot
snow
play
bath
birth

man
room
time
ball → football
day

18

Now pull this word apart to make two small words.

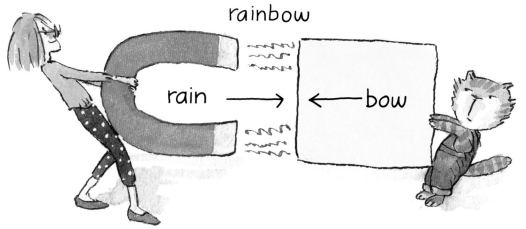

rainbow

rain → ← bow

Look at these words. See how they are made up.

> yourself   farmyard   postcard
>
> outside   indoors   nobody

Say the words.

Cover them.

Write each one.

Check your spelling.

Challenge

Break each word into two small words.

> yourself → your self

Letter patterns 'ain' and 'oin'

Look   Say   Cover   **Write**   Check

How good is your memory?
Look at this picture.

train

ointment

chain

coins

Looking for clues!

Look for the different letter patterns.

Close your eyes and picture the letter patterns.

Say the words slowly and clearly.

Write the words without copying.

Check your spelling.

Using the evidence 'ain' and 'oin'. . .

ain   oin

These words have lost their letter patterns.
Use the evidence to complete them.

p———   r———   j———

j———t   ag———

Write the finished words without copying.

'ain' words	'oin' words

Challenge

Finish this word with 'ain' or 'oin'.

p ———t   What is special?

Case closed

**Remember:
letter patterns help you to spell better.**

Nouns ending in 'y'

Be wise! Use your eyes
when dealing with 'y's.

I spy some things that end in 'y'.

boy

tray

donkey

Write the words in your book without copying.

A word that means more than one is
called a plural.

See how the plurals of these words are written.

donkeys

trays

boys

Write the plurals in your book without copying.
What is special about each letter before the 'y'?

Look carefully at the words
on the labels.
Write them in your book without copying.

What is special about each letter before the 'y'?

Look how the plurals are written.

ladies   flies   babies

Write the plurals without copying.

What can you say about changing words that
end in 'y' into plurals?

Try to make up a Handy Hint about it.

Now use it to make these words plural.

boy

puppy

day

key

sky

alley

city

Letter patterns 'ay' and 'oy'

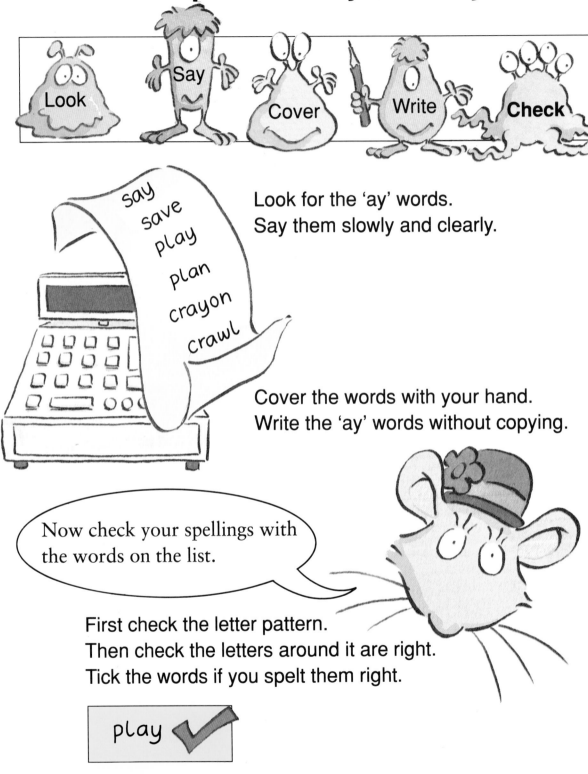

Look | Say | Cover | Write | **Check**

say
save
play
plan
crayon
crawl

Look for the 'ay' words.
Say them slowly and clearly.

Cover the words with your hand.
Write the 'ay' words without copying.

Now check your spellings with the words on the list.

First check the letter pattern.
Then check the letters around it are right.
Tick the words if you spelt them right.

play ✓

How many did you spell correctly?

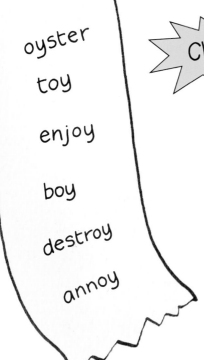

oyster

toy

enjoy

boy

destroy

annoy

Challenge

Look carefully at the 'oy' words.
Say the words.

When you think you can remember
the spelling, cover the words.

Write them without copying.
Use the list to check your spelling.

Now do the same for
these 'ay' words.

way

today

tray

always

holiday

yesterday

Case closed

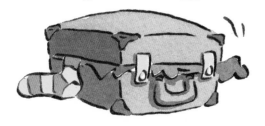

Always check your spelling.

**If there is a mistake write
the word again.**

Helping Harry: alphabetical order

Harry makes a list of the words he gets wrong each week.
Then he can learn to spell them correctly.

Harry writes the words in alphabetical order.

Challenge

Help Harry by writing these words correctly and in alphabetical order.

where	every	took
friend	school	

When writing each word:

Look at it.

Say it to yourself.
Try to see it in your mind.

Cover it up.

Write it from memory.

Look back and **check** the spelling. Start by checking the letter pattern.

Harry's word book

I tried to write last week's list in alphabetical order but I got some words in the wrong place.

horrible
baby
people
nearly
quickly

Write the words in alphabetical order.

Check your spellings afterwards.

Here are some 'c' words.
Look at them carefully. What do you notice?
Discuss it with a friend.

c

caravan
cheese
clown
computer
crisps
cupboard

Look carefully at the words.
Practise spelling them.
Ask a partner to choose three
and to test your spelling.
Check your spelling with
this list afterwards.

Write these 'd' words in alphabetical order without copying.

Challenge

drive   dish   day   dump   donkey   deep

Rhyming words

Words that rhyme sometimes have the same
letter patterns in them.

Find the rhyming words in these nursery rhymes.

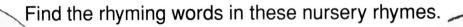

Hickory dickory dock
The mouse ran up the clock.

Humpty Dumpty sat on the wall.
Humpty Dumpty had a great fall.

Write the rhyming words and underline the
letter patterns that are the same.

Look at these two groups of words.

spell
bring
bone
school
black
small
mother

telephone
track
brother
smell
call
fool
fling

Write them without copying.

Join up the words that rhyme.

What can you say about each rhyming pair?

Sometimes words can rhyme and sound alike but do not have the same letter patterns.

> Baa, baa, black sheep, have you any wool?
> Yes Sir! Yes Sir! Three bags full.

> There was an old woman who lived in a shoe.
> She had so many children she didn't know what to do.

Find the rhyming words and write them.

What can you say about each pair?

Write out these two groups of words without copying.

Join up the words that rhyme.

noise
here
wool
eight

near
enjoys
late
bull

Add another rhyming word to each pair.

Putting it together: LaSaCaWaC

Here is a secret code to help with your spelling.

Copy out the code.

Look carefully at the word you want to learn.
Pick out the letter pattern.

and

Say the word.
Listen to the sound it makes.

and

Cover the word and memorize it.

and

Write the word from memory.

and

Check to see if you spelt it correctly.

Look and **Say** and **Cover** and **Write** and **Check**

Practise saying **LaSaCaWaC!**

Remember what all the letters stand for.

Now **LaSaCaWaC** these 'ard' words.

card
garden
hard
reward
mustard

Look again at page 30, then use **LaSaCaWaC** to learn these words.

party   smart   depart   chart

What letter pattern do they all have?

Case closed

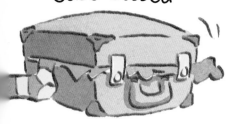

When you have new words to spell, LaSaCaWaC them!

Days of the week

How did they get their names?

Sun's day
Sunday

The sun was so important that people named the first day of the week after it.

Moon's day
Monday

People worshipped the moon long ago and named a day after it.

Tiwes' day
Tuesday

Tiwes, an old Viking god, gave his name to this day.

Woden's day
Wednesday

This day is named after Woden, who was king of all the Viking gods.

Thor's day
Thursday

Thor was the Viking god of thunder and this day was named after him.

Frigg's day
Friday

This day is named for Frigg, Viking goddess of love.

The name of each day sounds like the god it was called after.

LaSaCaWaC the days of the week.

Saturn's day
Saturday

Saturn was one of the Roman gods and this day was named for him.

See you again soon!